£2.95 nv

Music Theory in Practice

Grade 2

ERIC TAYLOR

The Associated Board of the Royal Schools of Music

2 304452 21

Syllabus for Grade 2

As in Grade 1, with the addition of:

(1) Simple time signatures of $\frac{2}{2}$ $\frac{3}{2}$ $\frac{4}{2}$ $\frac{3}{8}$, and the grouping of notes and rests within these times. Triplets and triplet note groups with rests. Questions will include the composition of simple four-bar rhythms starting on the first beat of the bar and using a given opening.

(2) Extension of the stave to include two ledger lines below and above each stave.

(3) Construction of the minor scale (harmonic or melodic at candidate's choice, but candidates will be expected to know which form they are using). Scales and key signatures of the major keys of A, B♭ and E♭, and the minor keys of A, E and D, with their tonic triads (root position), degrees (number only), and intervals above the tonic (by number only).

(4) More terms and signs in common use.

First published in 1990 by
The Associated Board of the Royal Schools of Music (Publishing) Ltd

Reprinted in 1992, 1994, 1995, 1996, 1997, 1998, 1999, 2000, 2002, 2003

© 1990 The Associated Board of the Royal Schools of Music

ISBN 1 85472 491 6

Typesetting and music processing by Halstan & Co. Ltd, Amersham, Bucks
Printed in Great Britain by Headley Brothers Ltd, Ashford, Kent

Contents

Thanks are due to the following publishers for permission to reprint extracts from copyright works: Boosey & Hawkes Music Publishers Ltd; Music Sales Ltd; Oxford University Press.

The music on the cover is the opening of an arrangement for trumpet in D and piano by Philip Cranmer of the aria, 'The trumpet shall sound', from Handel's *Messiah* (*Handel and Bach Arias*, published by the Associated Board)

In the quoted music examples, tempo marks without brackets occur in the original as shown. Tempo marks in brackets occur earlier in the music or are editorial.

A Ledger lines

(see *The AB Guide to Music Theory*, 2/1)

Grade 2 exercises may use up to two ledger lines above or below the stave.

Exercise 1 Under each of the following notes, write its name. The letter name alone is sufficient, if there is no accidental (e.g. 'F' means 'F natural'); but if there *is* an accidental, it must be included (e.g. 'F sharp' or 'F♯').

When you draw ledger lines, make sure that they do not slope up or down. They should be the same distance apart as the stave lines. Practise by writing a semibreve for every note between these:

Exercise 2 After each of the following notes, write the same note in the other clef (as shown in the answer to the first example).

Exercise 3 Rewrite the following in the bass clef, but at the same pitch. (As an illustration, the answer to the opening of the first example is given.)

Exercise 4 Rewrite the following in the treble clef, but at the same pitch.

B Time signatures: $\frac{2}{2}$, $\frac{3}{2}$, $\frac{4}{2}$, $\frac{3}{8}$

(see *The AB Guide to Music Theory*, 1/2)

All the time signatures which we have used so far have taken a crotchet as the sign for one beat. Grade 2 adds some time signatures in which the beat can be a minim or a quaver.

Music with two beats in a bar is always said to be in 'duple' time, no matter whether the beats are minims, crotchets or quavers. Similarly, music with three beats in a bar is always in 'triple' time, and music with four beats in a bar is always in 'quadruple' time.

Exercise 5   What does the 2 in $\frac{3}{2}$ mean? ....

What does the 8 in $\frac{3}{8}$ mean? ....

Give the full meaning of $\frac{4}{2}$ . ...

Show how the time signature sometimes shown as ¢ may be written in figures. ....

Explain the difference between $\frac{4}{4}$ and $\frac{2}{2}$ by completing the following:

$\frac{4}{4}$ means ....

$\frac{2}{2}$ means ....

Exercise 6   Add the time signature to each of the following.

(a)   Gibbons, Song 1

(b)   Allegretto   Mahler, Symphony No.4 (3rd mvt)

(c)   (Adagio)   Sibelius, Symphony No.7

©Edition Wilhelm Hansen AS

(d)   Presto   J. S. Bach, Italian Concerto (3rd mvt)

Exercise 6
(continued)

Exercise 7 Add the missing bar-lines in the following, which all start on the first beat of the bar.

Although written differently, these sound exactly the same:

Exercise 8   Rewrite each of the following rhythms using the new time signature, but making sure that the rhythm will sound the same. Then complete the sentence underneath by adding one of these words: duple, triple, quadruple.

Both of these are in .... time.

Both of these are in .... time.

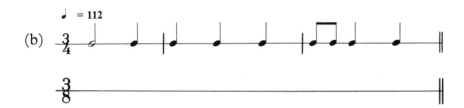

Both of these are in .... time.

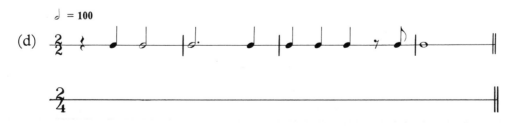

Both of these are in .... time.

C The major keys of A, B♭ and E♭

(see *The AB Guide to Music Theory*, 4/1)

Exercise 9   Add accidentals where needed to make the scales named. (Do not use key signatures.)
Then draw ⌐‾‾‾¬ over each pair of notes making a semitone.

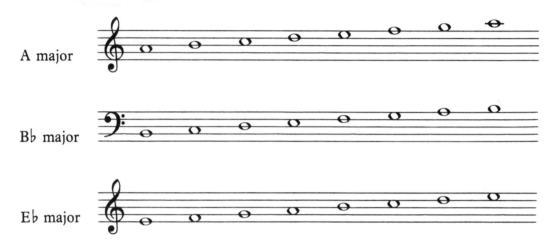

A major

B♭ major

E♭ major

Exercise 10   Name the major keys shown by the following key signatures. After each write the key-note
followed by the tonic triad (as shown in the answer to the first example).

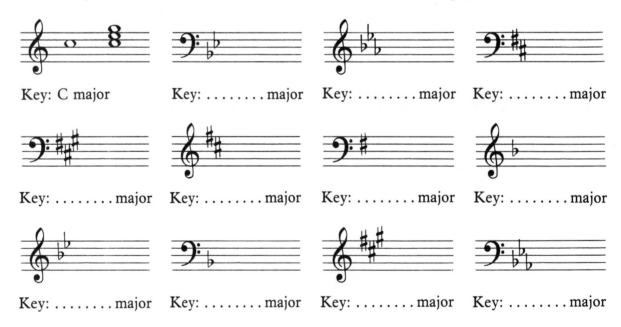

Key: C major

Key: .... major

Key: .... major

Key: .... major

Key: .... major

Key: .... major

Key: .... major

Key: .... major

Key: .... major

Key: .... major

Key: .... major

Key: .... major

Notice that key signatures with three sharps are written:

and (NOT or , or in any other way).

Similarly, key signatures with two flats are written:

and

Exercise 11   Add the clefs and key signatures needed to make the major scales of the keys named.

A major

E♭ major

B♭ major

A major

E♭ major

B♭ major

Exercise 12   Name the key of each of the following. Then write them out again, using key signatures instead of accidentals.

Schubert, Symphony No.5 (1st mvt)

(a)

Key . . . .

Waldteufel, *The Skaters Waltz*

(b)

Key . . . .

Exercise 12
(continued)

(c) Wagner, *The Mastersingers* (Act III Prelude)
(Poco adagio)

Key . . . .

(d) Chopin, Waltz, Op.18
Vivo
etc.

Key . . . .

(e) Beethoven, Cello Sonata, Op.69 No.3 (1st mvt)
Allegro, ma non tanto
etc.

Key . . . .

(f) Walford Davies, *R.A.F. March Past*
Quick ♩ = 132

© Copyright 1921 Boosey & Co. Ltd
Reproduced by permission of Boosey & Hawkes Music Publishers Ltd.

Key . . . .

(g) Franck, Violin Sonata (4th mvt)
Allegretto poco mosso
etc.

Key . . . .

(h) Elgar, Symphony No.2 (4th mvt)
Moderato e maestoso

Key . . . .

D Triplets

(see *The AB Guide to Music Theory*, 3/3)

Exercise 13 Write ONE note which will last as long as each of these groups of notes.

♩♩♩ are played in the time of a . . . .

♩♩♩ are played in the time of a . . . .

♩♩♩ are played in the time of a . . . .

𝅗𝅥𝅗𝅥𝅗𝅥 are played in the time of a . . . .

♩ ⁊ ♩ are played in the time of a . . . .

♩ ⁊ ♩ are played in the time of a . . . .

♩. ♪♪ are played in the time of a . . . .

It is not necessary to draw a slur or bracket over or below the 3, when notes making a triplet are beamed together. But a slur or bracket is usually added if the groups consist of separate notes, or of a mixture of notes and rests.

Exercise 14 Add a triplet sign where it is needed to make these bars fit their time signatures.

14

E The minor keys of A, E and D

(see *The AB Guide to Music Theory*, 4/2)

There is only one scale for each major key, and its notes are the same whether it goes up or down. But a minor key has two: the 'harmonic' minor scale and the 'melodic' minor scale. Also, the descending form of the melodic minor scale is different from its ascending form. As examples, here are the scales of A major and A minor, with the semitones marked ⌐⎯⎤ .

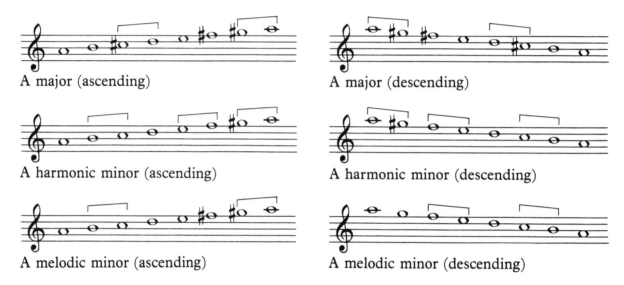

A major (ascending)   A major (descending)

A harmonic minor (ascending)   A harmonic minor (descending)

A melodic minor (ascending)   A melodic minor (descending)

In this grade you do not have to know *both* forms of the minor scale: you may choose either the harmonic or the melodic form. But you will need to know the name of the form you are using – either harmonic or melodic.

Exercise 15   Using the given rhythm, write either the harmonic or the melodic minor scale in each of the keys named below. In the brackets write the name of the form (harmonic or melodic) which you have used. Do not use key signatures: write separate accidentals for notes which need them, and add ⌐⎯⎤ signs to mark the semitones.

A minor (........ form) ascending

D minor (........ form) ascending

E minor (........ form) ascending

D minor
(. . . . . form)
descending

E minor
(. . . . . . . form)
descending

Exercise 16 Using the given rhythms, write either the harmonic or the melodic form of the scale in each of the keys named below. In the brackets write the name of the form (harmonic or melodic) which you have used. Write in the correct key signature in each case. Do not add unnecessary accidentals, but remember that the key signature of a minor key does not include all the accidentals which may be needed.

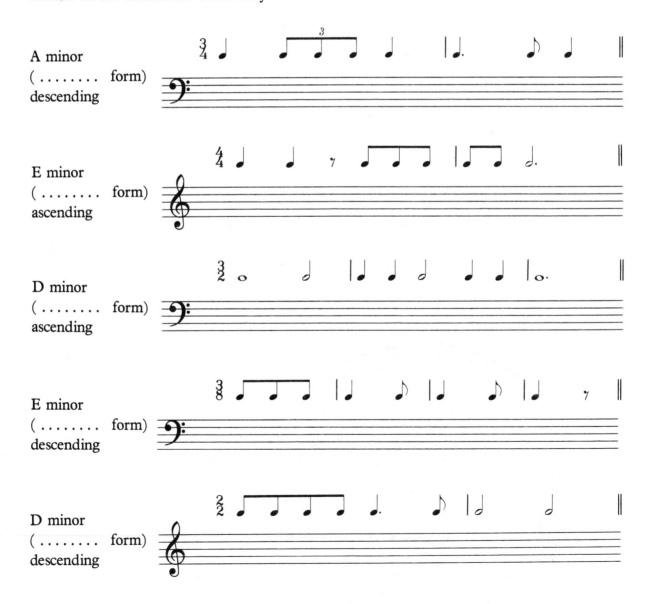

A minor
(. . . . . . . form)
descending

E minor
(. . . . . . . form)
ascending

D minor
(. . . . . . . form)
ascending

E minor
(. . . . . . . form)
descending

D minor
(. . . . . . . form)
descending

As in major scales, the first note of a minor scale is called the 'key-note' or '1st degree' or 'tonic'. Similarly, the tonic triad of a minor key consists of its key-note plus the 3rd and 5th degrees of the scale above it.

Note also that the terms 'harmonic' and 'melodic' refer only to scales, *not to keys*. A piece may be 'in the key of D minor', for example, or just in 'D minor'; but it would be wrong to say that it is 'in the key of D harmonic minor' or 'in the key of D melodic minor'.

Exercise 17   Name the minor keys shown by the following key signatures. After each, write its key-note followed by the tonic triad.

Key: . . . . minor   Key: . . . . minor   Key: . . . . minor

Key: . . . . minor   Key: . . . . minor   Key: . . . . minor

Exercise 18   Name the key of each of the following. Except for any examples in A minor, write them out again, using the correct key signature. Leave out any unnecessary accidentals, but remember to add any that may be needed.

(Andantino)   Schumann, *Album for the Young* ('Erster Verlust')

(a)

Key . . . .

Allegro assai   Haydn, *The Creation* ('Rolling in foaming billows')

(b)

Key . . . .

(c)

Key . . . .

(d)

Key . . . .

(e)

Key . . . .

(f)

Key . . . .

(g)

Key . . . .

F Grouping of notes and rests

(see *The AB Guide to Music Theory*, 5/1–3)

The elementary uses of beams, ties and dots were introduced in Grade 1 (see *Music Theory in Practice*, Grade 1, Section P). Now some more information is needed to cover the new time signatures – $\frac{2}{2}$, $\frac{3}{2}$, $\frac{4}{2}$, $\frac{3}{8}$ – and also some other problems which may arise in Grade 2.

The main points to remember about the grouping of notes are as follows.

(1) In time signatures with a minim beat ($\frac{2}{2}$, $\frac{3}{2}$, $\frac{4}{2}$):

(a) Always use a semibreve (not two tied minims) where possible –

(b) Beam together a group of 4 quavers, which could be replaced by a minim –

Similarly, beam together 4 semiquavers, which could be replaced by a crotchet –

Do not beam together more than 4 quavers.

(2) In $\frac{3}{8}$, beam together quavers and/or semiquavers making a complete bar –

(3) Except for $\frac{3}{8}$ , do not beam together more than 4 semiquavers

In the above examples of beams, the notes were printed simply as rhythms.
When the notes are written on a stave, however, a new problem can arise. Consider, for example:

Here the stems of the first two notes go down, but the stem of the last note goes up.
But when notes are beamed together, *all* the stems in the group go either up or down – usually according to what suits most of them. Thus, these three notes would be beamed:

Similarly, would normally become rather than :

the first note 'wins' because it is further from the middle line of the stave.

These are the main points to remember about the arrangement of rests:

(1) If you need to show a complete bar's rest, it should be written | ▬ |,

thus –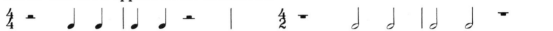

(A bar's rest in 4/2 is written differently, but this will not be used until Grade 4.)

(2) In quadruple time, a two-beat rest should be used if the first half of the bar is silent. The same applies to the second half –

(3) Everywhere else, a new beat always needs a new rest –

(4) Where rests of less than a beat are used, group the notes and rests in half-beats (shown below by ⌐▬⌐).

(These are also not strictly correct – although they are occasionally found in printed music.)

(5) Do not use more rests than are needed by the rules above. For example, write –

(6) Groups of notes which can be beamed together can still be beamed together when a rest is used instead of a note. The most common example is

Exercise 19 Rewrite the following, putting right any mistakes in the grouping of the notes and rests. (As an illustration, the answer to the first example is given.)

G Intervals

(see *The AB Guide to Music Theory*, 7/1)

If you play a note, and then play a higher or lower note, the distance in pitch between them is called an 'interval'. It is a 'melodic' interval if the two notes are played one after the other, or a 'harmonic' interval if they are played together. The size of an interval is measured by the number of degrees of the scale it includes, for example:

2nd   3rd   4th   5th

The number of degrees is the 'number' of the interval. It is not affected by the key signature, or by any sharps, flats or naturals which the notes may have before them. In Grade 2 we will use only those intervals which have the key-note as the lower note. Therefore, the number of the interval will always be the same as the degree of the scale on which the top note is placed. For example, here are the intervals from the key-note in G major:

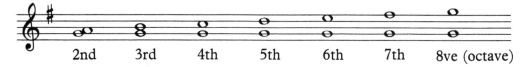

2nd   3rd   4th   5th   6th   7th   8ve (octave)

And similarly in A minor –

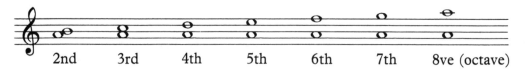

2nd   3rd   4th   5th   6th   7th   8ve (octave)

(In A minor, of course, both the F and the G might be sharpened, depending on which form of the scale is being used; but this would not affect the *number* of the interval.)

Exercise 20   Give the number of each of the following intervals. The lower note is the key-note.

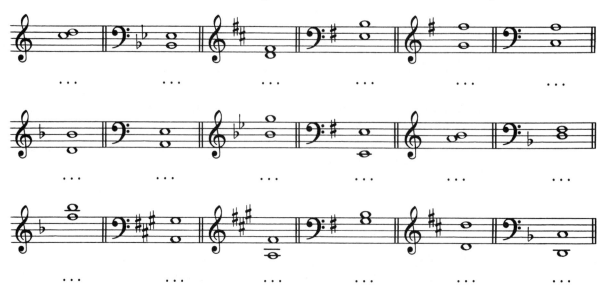

Intervals are always counted from the lower note – even if, in a melodic interval, the upper note comes first. Thus both of these are intervals of a 6th:

Exercise 21   Give the number of each of the intervals marked ⌐──¬ in the following.

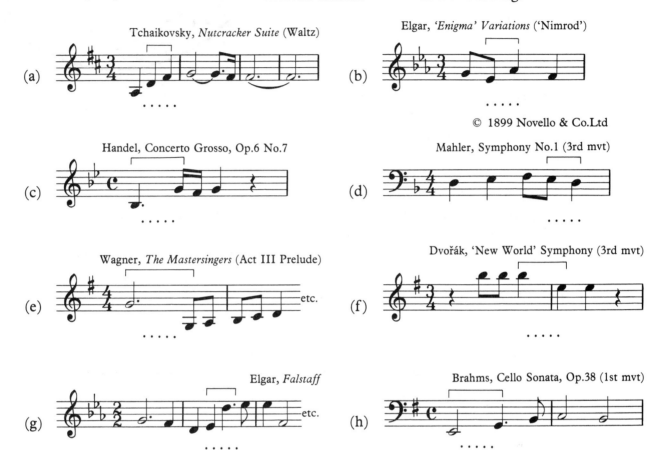

© 1899 Novello & Co.Ltd

H Composing simple four-bar rhythms

In Grade 1, you were given a two-bar rhythm and asked to add another two bars as an answering rhythm. The Grade 2 test is a little different. You will be given only the first bar, or possibly even less. The given opening will start on the first beat of the bar, and you will be asked to continue it to make a four-bar rhythm.

The rhythm you write must have some feeling of design: it is not enough to fill up four bars with an assortment of notes which do nothing more than fit in with the time signature. This,

for example, is musically shapeless –

Yet to have no variety – – is dull.

There is no single or guaranteed way of composing an interesting and well-balanced four-bar rhythm. Your ear is your best guide, and you are unlikely to succeed unless you have 'heard' your rhythm in your head. But it may help you to look at the examples on the next page.

You will realise from any of these melodies which you happen to know that only the beginning is given. Often the first four bars are followed by another four, to make eight; and these eight bars are followed by another eight, making sixteen; and so on.

Notice the following features in the melodies quoted opposite (the letters refer to the examples, but now only their rhythms are shown).

(1) The rhythms all end *on a beat*, with a note which lasts at least a full beat (or perhaps ♪𝄾 instead of ♩). This helps to make the four bars feel like a single unit, similar to a line of verse.

(2) Sometimes the rhythm of bars 1 and 2 is repeated exactly in bars 3 and 4:

Thus the four bars are divided into two two-bar sections.

(3) A similar impression is created if the two sections merely *start* in the same way:

or finish in the same way:

(e) [rhythm notation]

(4) Other repetitions of single bars are also common:

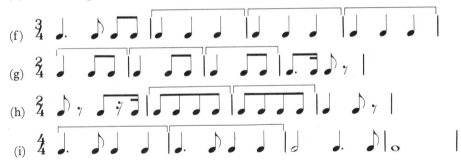

It must be emphasised that these points show only a few of the possibilities. Although they are all very common, music provides many others, including examples where there are *no* repetitions of complete bars:

Exercise 22 In each of the following, add ⌐￢ signs (as in the examples on the previous page) to show any bars with the same rhythm. If the rhythm of bars 1 + 2 is the same as the rhythm of bars 3 + 4, write ⌐￢ over each of the pairs. Where there are no repetitions at all, put a × at the end.

Dvořák, *Slavonic Dance*, Op.46 No.1

(a)

Holst, hymn tune 'Cranham'

(b)

Allegro giusto   Debussy, *Children's Corner Suite* ('Golliwog's Cake-Walk')

(c)

Allegro molto moderato   Grieg, Piano Concerto (1st mvt)

(d)

Allegro moderato   Stravinsky (after Pergolesi), *Pulcinella* (Gavotte)

(e)

© Copyright 1924 by Hawkes & Son (London) Ltd
Revised version © Copyright 1949 by Hawkes & Son (London) Ltd
Reproduced by permission of Boosey & Hawkes Music Publishers Ltd.

Mozart, Minuet, K.3

(f)

Lent ♩ = 58   Ravel, *Mother Goose* (Pavane)

(g)

Reproduced by permission of Editions Durand S.A., Paris/United Music Publishers Ltd.

Mozart, Clarinet Concerto (2nd mvt)

Adagio

(h)

In the exercise on the next page, make several workings of each of the openings on your own paper before completing one in this book. A moderate speed will always be suitable. However, if you particularly want a very slow or a very quick speed, give it a tempo direction. This could be a metronome mark or a word such as *Allegro*, *Lento* etc. Test your rhythms by tapping them out, and always be sure that you can 'hear' what you write.

Exercise 23 Continue each of the following openings to create four-bar rhythms. Experiment with
(1) different types of repetition, and (2) rhythms in which no two bars are the same.

▮ Performance directions

(see *The AB Guide to Music Theory*, 10 and 11)

In Grade 2, you will be expected to know the following words and signs, in addition to those given in Grade 1. The words below are all Italian.

a	at, to, by, for, in, in the style of
al, alla	to the, in the manner of (*alla marcia*: in the style of a march)
allargando	broadening (getting a little slower and probably a little louder)
andantino	slightly faster than *Andante* (but may also mean slightly slower)
assai	very (*allegro assai*: very quick)
con, col	with
dolce	sweet, soft
e, ed	and
espressivo (or *espress.* or *espr.*)	expressive
fp (= *fortepiano*)	loud, then immediately soft
giocoso	playful, merry
grave	very slow, solemn
grazioso	graceful
larghetto	rather slow (but not as slow as *largo*)
largo	slow, stately
ma	but
maestoso	majestic
meno	less
molto	very, much
mosso, moto	movement (*meno mosso*: slower; *con moto*: with movement)
non	not
più	more
presto	fast (faster than *Allegro*)
senza	without
sf, sfz (= *sforzando* or *sforzato*)	forced, accented
simile (or *sim.*)	in the same way
sostenuto	sustained
tenuto	held
troppo	too much (*non troppo*: not too much)
vivace, vivo	lively, quick

Below are some signs you should know in Grade 2.

 The sign > over or under a note means that it is to be accented.
∧ (over) and v (under) mean the same, or even stronger accents.

 Dots inside a slur mean that the notes should be slightly separated (semi-staccato), but less so than notes with ordinary staccato dots.

A wedge sign ▾ indicates a super-staccato (staccatissimo): the note is to be played as briefly as possible and perhaps accented as well.

The sign – means that the note is to be given a slight pressure (and generally slightly separated).

J General exercises

Exercise 24   This is the beginning of a melody. Look at it, and then answer the questions below.

(a) What key is the melody in? ....

(b) Which bar has only notes belonging to the tonic triad? .....

(c) Draw circles round two notes next to each other which make the interval of an octave.

(d) Draw ⌐‾‾‾¬ over any pair of notes which make a semitone.

(e) Which bar has an accented note? .....

(f) What is the Italian word for the sign ━━ in the last bar? ....

What does it mean? ....

(g) Which bars have a different rhythm from the first one? ....

(h) What is *mf* short for? .... What does it mean? ....

(i) What is the letter name of the last note in bar 4? .....

Show how this note would be written in the bass clef. 𝄢 ═════

Exercise 25   Look at this melody, and then answer the questions below.

Bartók, For Children, Vol.I No.11

(a)   Give the meaning of the following words and signs:

Lento   ....

♩ = 66   ....

dolce   ....

molto espr.   ....

◁   ....

▷   ....

− −   (below notes in bars 8 and 12)   ....

mp   ....

(b)   Which bars have only notes belonging to the tonic triad? ....

(c)   Cross out any of the following time values which are NOT used in this melody:
      semibreve; minim; crotchet; quaver; semiquaver.

(d)   What is the interval (number only) between the first two notes? .....

(e)   Which other pairs of bars have the same rhythm as bars 1–2? ....

(f)   Draw ⌐‾¬ over two notes next to each other which make the interval of an octave.

(g)   Copy out from bar 9 to the end, but do not use a key signature. (Remember to write
      accidentals before notes which need them.)

Exercise 26 This melody is played by cellos during the course of the last movement of Dvořák's 8th Symphony. Look at it, and then answer the questions below.

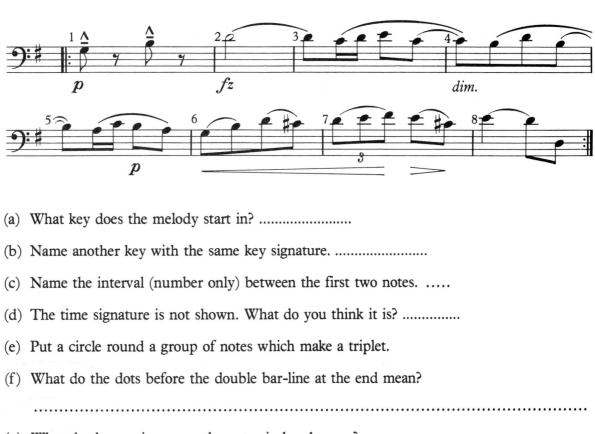

(a) What key does the melody start in? ....

(b) Name another key with the same key signature. ....

(c) Name the interval (number only) between the first two notes. ......

(d) The time signature is not shown. What do you think it is? ....

(e) Put a circle round a group of notes which make a triplet.

(f) What do the dots before the double bar-line at the end mean?

     ....

(g) What do the ∧ signs over the notes in bar 1 mean?

     ....

(h) How many pairs of notes are tied? ....

     Give their letter names. ....

(i) The tempo direction at the beginning of the movement is *Allegro, ma non troppo*.
    Underline which of these you think is the best translation:
    very quick;   not quick;   quick, but not loud;   quick, but not too quick.

(j) Copy out bars 6 and 7 in the treble clef, putting in the key signature.

Exercise 27   This is the beginning of a melody. Look at it, and then answer the questions below.

Kenneth J. Alford, *Colonel Bogey*

(a) What is the meaning of ¢ ? ....

(b) This is a quick march. Choose one of the following words as a suitable tempo direction, and add it in the correct place in the music:
Adagio, Allegro, Andante, Larghetto, Presto.

(c) What key is the melody in? ....

(d) Show how the key signature of this music is written in the bass clef.
Then show how the last two notes of bar 2 would be written in the bass clef.

(e) Draw a circle round three notes next to each other which make a tonic triad.

(f) Give the pitch name of the highest note. ....

(g) What does the sign > above or under notes mean? ....

(h) What do you notice about bars 9–12 compared to bars 5–8?

....

(i) After each of these rests write a note of the same value.

᾽ ....   ≀ ....   ▬ ....

(j) Rewrite the rhythm of bars 1–4 using the new time signature given below.
Make sure that the rhythm sounds the same.

$\frac{2}{4}$